Lyric Poems

Lyric Poems

Selected by Coralie Howard

Illustrated by Mel Fowler

FRANKLIN WATTS, INC.

575 Lexington Avenue · New York, N.Y. 10022

ACKNOWLEDGMENTS

The selections in this book are used by permission and special arrangements with the proprietors of their respective copyrights who are listed below. Any requests for use of this material in any form must be directed to the copyright holders who are listed herein. The editor's and publisher's thanks to all who made this collection possible.

The editor and publisher have made every effort to trace the ownership of all material collected herein. It is their belief that the necessary permissions from publishers, authors, and authorized agents have been obtained in all cases. In the event of any questions arising as to the use of any material, the editor and publisher express regret for any error unconsciously made and will be pleased to make the necessary correction in future editions of this book.

The American–Scandinavian Foundation, for "The Plants Stand Silent Round Me," by Johannes Jörgensen, from *A Book of Danish Verse,* compiled by Oluf Friis, translated by S. Foster Damon and Robert Hillyer.

Brandt and Brandt, for "Daniel Boone," by Stephen Vincent Benet. From *A Book of Americans* by Rosemary and Stephen Vincent Benet (Holt, Rinehart and Winston, Inc.). Copyright © 1933 by Rosemary and Stephen Vincent Benet. Copyright renewed 1961 by Rosemary Carr Benet.

Charles Scribner's Sons, for "As Birds are Fitted to the Boughs," from *Good News of Death and Other Poems* by Louis Simpson, POETS OF TODAY II; (Copyright © 1955 Louis Simpson); "Leaf and Sun" (Copyright 1954 Norma Farber) and "The Hatch" (Copyright 1953 Norma Farber) from *The Hatch: Poems* by Norma Farber, POETS OF TODAY II; "Bits of Glass" (Copyright © 1956 Spencer Brown) from *My Father's Business and Other Poems* by Spencer Brown, POETS OF TODAY III; and "The March Problem" (Copyright © 1956 *The Carolina Quarterly*) from *The Reverend Ghost: Poems* by George Garrett, POETS OF TODAY IV. All reprinted with the permission of Charles Scribner's Sons.

IV

Clarendon Press, Oxford, for "My Love," by Ono No Yoshiki, from *Japanese Poems*, translated by Arthur Waley. Reprinted by permission of the Clarendon Press, Oxford.

Collins-Knowlton-Wing, Inc. and Robert Graves, for "Flying Crooked" and "Traveller's Curse after Misdirection," from *Collected Poems of Robert Graves* (Doubleday & Company, Inc. and Cassell & Co. Ltd.), copyright © 1955 by International Authors, N.V.

Columbia University Press, for "The Night Is Darkening Round Me," from *The Complete Poems of Emily Brontë*, edited by C. W. Hatfield.

The Cresset Press Limited, for "The Lost Tribe," from *Urania* (1950), by Ruth Pitter.

Crown Publishers, Inc., for "March Weather," from *A Land and a People* by Shirley Barker. © 1952 by Shirley Barker. Used by permission of Crown Publishers, Inc.

The Dial Press, Inc., for "A Talisman," reprinted from *Observations* by Marianne Moore. Copyright 1924 by Marianne Moore and used by permission of the publishers, The Dial Press, Inc.

Doubleday & Company, Inc., for "The Heron," copyright 1937 by Theodore Roethke; "Root Cellar," copyright 1943 by Modern Poetry Association, Inc.; and "Night Crow," copyright 1944 by Saturday Review Association, Inc., all from the book, *The Collected Poems of Theodore Roethke*. Reprinted by permission of Doubleday & Company, Inc.

E. P. Dutton & Co., Inc., for "Signs of Winter," from the book *The Poems of John Clare* (1793–1864) edited by J. W. Tibble. Published by E. P. Dutton & Co., Inc. and reprinted with their permission.

Farrar, Straus & Giroux, Inc., for "Question in a Field," copyright 1937 by The New Yorker Magazine, Inc., renewed 1964 by Louise Bogan; "Variation on a Sentence," copyright 1936 by The New Yorker Magazine, Inc., renewed 1954 by Louise Bogan, from *Collected Poems*, by Louise Bogan; and "Closing of the Rodeo," from *Celebration at Dark* by William Jay Smith. First printed in Great Britain. All reprinted with permission of Farrar, Straus & Giroux, Inc.

George Allen Unwin Ltd., for "My Love," from *Chinese Poems*, translated by Arthur Waley.

Grove Press, Inc., for "Changing the Wheel" and "Iron" by Bertolt Brecht, translated by Michael Hamburger, from *Modern German Poetry*, edited by Michael Hamburger and Christopher Middleton. Reprinted by permission of Grove Press, Inc. Copyright © 1962 by Michael Hamburger and Christopher Middleton.

Harcourt, Brace & World, Inc., for "pity this busy monster," copyright, 1944, by E. E. Cummings, and "Buffalo Bill's," copyright 1923, 1951, by E. E. Cummings. Reprinted from his volume *Poems 1923–1954* by permission of Harcourt, Brace & World, Inc.; "Hazardous Occupations," by Carl Sandburg From *Slabs of the Sunburnt West* by Carl

V

VIII

CONTENTS

XII

XIII

FOREWORD

Poetry is a pattern of words that recreates an emotion. In lyric poetry the emotion is even more direct and intense than in other kinds of poetry. The word "lyric," in connection with poetry, once referred only to a song. Now we may call any subjective, emotional poem a lyric. Usually it is short, songlike, and expressive of a single mood.

In this collection are lyrics from many languages and times. The oldest are several thousand years old, while many are by living poets. What they all have in common is brevity and intensity.

Because in these poems so much is condensed in a few lines, it is necessary to read them carefully. To get the most from a poem, read it aloud, and most important, read it again and again.

The poet Robert Frost said, "Like a piece of ice on a hot stove the poem must ride on its own melting." And so to the lyrics themselves—may you enjoy them.

C. H.

XV

LOVE LYRIC

TRANSLATED FROM THE ANCIENT EGYPTIAN
BY NOEL STOCK

Nothing, nothing can keep me from my love
Standing on the other shore.

Not even old crocodile
There on the sandbank between us
Can keep us apart.

I go in spite of him,
I walk upon the waves,
Her love flows back across the water,
Turning waves to solid earth
For me to walk on.

The river is our Enchanted Sea.

PAPAGO LOVE SONG

TRANSLATED FROM THE PAPAGO INDIAN
BY MARY AUSTIN

Early I rose
In the blue morning;
My love was up before me,
It came running to me from the Doorways of the Dawn.

On Papago Mountain
The dying quarry
Looked at me with my love's eyes.

THE DALLIANCE OF THE LEOPARDS

Anonymous [*Fifth century* A.D.]

TRANSLATED FROM THE SANSKRIT
BY POWYS MATHERS

Very afraid
I saw the dalliance of the leopards.
In the beauty of their coats
They sought each other and embraced.
Had I gone between them then
And pulled them asunder by their manes,
I would have run less risk
Than when I passed in my boat
And saw you standing on a dead tree
Ready to dive and kindle the river.

MY LOVE
by Ono No Yoshiki [*died* A.D. *902*]

TRANSLATED FROM THE JAPANESE
BY ARTHUR WALEY

My love
Is like the grasses
Hidden in the deep mountain:
Though its abundance increases,
There is none that knows.

4

RONDEL

by Jean Froissart [1337–1404]

TRANSLATED FROM THE FRENCH
BY HENRY WADSWORTH LONGFELLOW

Love, love, what wilt thou with this heart of mine?
Naught see I fixed or sure in thee!
I do not know thee,—nor what deeds are thine:
Love, love, what wilt thou with this heart of mine?
    Naught see I fixed or sure in thee!

Shall I be mute, or vows with prayers combine?
    Ye who are blessed in loving, tell it me:
Love, love, what wilt thou with this heart of mine?
    Naught see I permanent or sure in thee!

THE LOWEST TREES HAVE TOPS
by Sir Edward Dyer [1545?–1607]

The lowest trees have tops, the ant her gall,
   The fly her spleen, the little sparks their heat;
The slender hairs cast shadows, though but small,
   And bees have stings, although they be not great,
Seas have their source, and so have shallow springs;
   And love is love, in beggars as in kings.

Where rivers smoothest run, deep are the fords;
   The dial stirs, yet none perceives it move;
The firmest faith is in the fewest words;
   The turtles cannot sing, and yet they love:
True hearts have eyes and ears, no tongues to speak,
They hear and see, and sigh, and then they break.

SONG FROM *TWELFTH NIGHT*
by William Shakespeare [1564–1616]

O mistress mine, where are you roaming?
Oh, stay and hear; your true love's coming,
  That can sing both high and low:
Trip no further, pretty sweeting;
Journeys end in lovers' meeting,
  Every wise man's son doth know.

What is love? 'tis not hereafter;
Present mirth hath present laughter;
  What's to come is still unsure:
In delay there lies no plenty;
Then come kiss me, sweet and twenty,
  Youth's a stuff will not endure.

SONNET

by William Shakespeare [1564–1616]

Devouring Time, blunt thou the lion's paws,
And make the earth devour her own sweet brood.
Pluck the keen teeth from the fierce tiger's jaws,
And burn the long-lived phoenix in her blood;
Make glad the sorry seasons as thou fleets,
And do whate'er thou wilt, swift-footed Time,
To the wide world and all her fading sweets;
But I forbid thee one most heinous crime:
O, carve not with thy hours my love's fair brow,
Nor draw no lines there with thine antique pen;
Him in thy course untainted do allow
For beauty's pattern to succeeding men.
Yet, do thy worst, old Time! despite thy wrong,
My love shall in my verse ever live young.

LOVEL'S SONG
by Ben Jonson [1573?–1637]

It was a beauty that I saw
   So pure, so perfect, as the frame
   Of all the universe was lame,
To that one figure, could I draw,
Or give least line of it a law!

A skein of silk without a knot.
   A fair march made without a halt.
   A curious form without a fault.
A printed book without a blot.
All beauty, and without a spot!

THE CONSTANT LOVER

by Sir John Suckling [1609–1642]

Out upon it! I have loved
   Three whole days together;
And am like to love three more,
   If it prove fair weather.

Time shall moult away his wings
   Ere he shall discover
In the whole wide world again
   Such a constant lover.

But the spite on 't is, no praise
   Is due at all to me;
Love with me had made no stays,
   Had it any been but she.

Had it any been but she,
   And that very face,
There had been at least ere this
   A dozen dozen in her place.

WHEN I LOVED YOU
by Thomas Moore [1779–1852]

When I loved you, I can't but allow
   I had many an exquisite minute;
But the scorn I feel for you now
   Hath even more luxury in it!

Thus, whether we're on or we're off,
   Some witchery seems to await you;
To love you is pleasant enough,
   And oh! 'tis delicious to hate you!

MEETING AT NIGHT
by Robert Browning [1812–1889]

The gray sea and the long black land;
And the yellow half-moon large and low;
And the startled little waves that leap
In fiery ringlets from their sleep,
As I gain the cove with pushing prow,
And quench its speed in the slushy sand.

Then a mile of warm sea-scented beach;
Three fields to cross till a farm appears;
A tap at the pane, the quick sharp scratch
And blue spurt of a lighted match,
And a voice less loud, through its joys and fears,
Than the two hearts beating each to each.

WHEN I WAS ONE-AND-TWENTY
by A. E. Housman [1859–1936]

When I was one-and-twenty
  I heard a wise man say,
"Give crowns and pounds and guineas
  But not your heart away;
Give pearls away and rubies
  But keep your fancy free."
But I was one-and-twenty,
  No use to talk to me.

When I was one-and-twenty
  I heard him say again,
"The heart out of the bosom
  Was never given in vain;
'Tis paid with sighs a plenty
  And sold for endless rue."
And I am two-and-twenty,
  And oh, 'tis true, 'tis true.

HE WISHES FOR THE
CLOTHS OF HEAVEN
by William Butler Yeats [1865–1939]

Had I the heavens' embroidered cloths,
Enwrought with gold and silver light,
The blue and the dim and the dark cloths
Of night and light and the half-light,
I would spread the cloths under your feet:
But I, being poor, have only my dreams;
I have spread my dreams under your feet;
Tread softly because you tread on my dreams.

THE SONG OF
WANDERING AENGUS

by William Butler Yeats [1865–1939]

I went out to the hazel wood,
Because a fire was in my head,
And cut and peeled a hazel wand,
And hooked a berry to a thread;
And when white moths were on the wing,
And moth-like stars were flickering out,
I dropped the berry in a stream
And caught a little silver trout.

When I had laid it on the floor
I went to blow the fire a-flame,
But something rustled on the floor,
And someone called me by my name:
It had become a glimmering girl
With apple blossom in her hair
Who called me by my name and ran
And faded through the brightening air.

Though I am old with wandering
Through hollow lands and hilly lands,
I will find out where she has gone,
And kiss her lips and take her hands;
And walk among long dappled grass,
And pluck till time and times are done
The silver apples of the moon,
The golden apples of the sun.

PUT OUT MY EYES
by Rainer Maria Rilke [1875–1926]

TRANSLATED FROM THE GERMAN
BY BABETTE DEUTSCH

Put out my eyes, and I can see you still;
slam my ears to, and I can hear you yet;
and without any feet can go to you;
and tongueless I can conjure you at will.
Break off my arms, I shall take hold of you
and grasp you with my heart as with a hand;
arrest my heart, my brain will beat as true;
and if you set this brain of mine afire,
then on my blood I yet will carry you.

LOSS

by Paul Eluard [1895–1952]

TRANSLATED FROM THE FRENCH
BY PATRICIA TERRY

Unknown, she was the form I preferred,
The one who drew from me the weight of being a man,
And I see her and I lose her and I suffer
My grief like a little sunlight in chill water.

WHEN TROUT SWIM DOWN
GREAT ORMOND STREET

by Conrad Aiken [1889–   ]

When trout swim down Great Ormond Street,
And sea-gulls cry above them lightly,
And hawthorns heave cold flagstones up
To blossom whitely

Against old walls of houses there,
Gustily shaking out in moonlight
Their country sweetness on sweet air;
And in the sunlight,

By the green margin of that water
Children dip white feet and shout,
Casting nets in the braided water
To catch the trout:

Then I shall hold my breath and die,
Swearing I never loved you; no,
'You were not lovely!' I shall cry,
'I never loved you so.'

17

SINCE MY BIRTH

by Yvan Goll [1891–1950]

TRANSLATED FROM THE FRENCH
BY CLAIRE GOLL

Since my birth
I have adorned myself
For your arrival
Ten thousand days
I have been walking out
To meet you

Countries have narrowed
Mountains have bowed
Rivers have shrunk

Only my body has grown beyond myself
And lies outstretched from dusk to daybreak
Covering the whole world

Wherever you go now
You walk on me

THE TURNING

by Philip Murray [1924–   ]

It was a day of turning when you came—
The clouds were rolling in the shifting sky;
The sun was spinning on the garden lawn
A net of leaf-light cast for your dark hair.
It was a day of movement everywhere—
The hills were dipping, rising, the river ran,
Leaped, moulded to rocks, and leaped again.
I felt the very earth beneath my feet then
Wheeling away to other parts of the world
In that one moment I would have caught and held.

AS BIRDS ARE FITTED
TO THE BOUGHS

by Louis Simpson [*1923–*   ]

As birds are fitted to the boughs
That blossom on the tree
And whisper when the south wind blows—
So was my love to me.

And still she blossoms in my mind
And whispers softly, though
The clouds are fitted to the wind,
The wind is to the snow.

MARCH WEATHER

by Shirley Barker [1911–   ]

Landscapes dissolve in rain,
Now winter splits apart;
Willows bud in the fen;
The weather in the heart
Stirs like the greening wave,
Quickens in kindled fire:
Now every girl believes
In every man's desire.

The leafless lilac hedge
Too bare to shelter love,
The sea-blown winds that rage
Inland cannot reprove
This shaft of mellowing light
Over inward acres blown.
In this weather of the heart
No lover goes alone.

THE PLANTS STAND
SILENT ROUND ME

by Johannes Jörgensen [1866–1956]

TRANSLATED FROM THE DANISH
BY ROBERT HILLYER

The plants stand silent round me,
And the tree with light green leaves
Where slanting sunlight scatters
Its dust in yellow sheaves.

Far bells ring faintly over
The basking summerlands,
Vast and green and breathless
Round me the forest stands.

Only a lonely throstle
Trilling in yonder tree.
In the air a smell of forests,
In my heart, ecstasy.

DEAD DOE

by Jim Harrison [1937–   ]

Amid pale green milkweed
wild clover
a rotted doe, curled,
shag-like
after a winter so cold
the trees split open.
I think she couldn't keep up
with the others—
they had no place to go—
and her food,
the frozen grass and twigs,
wouldn't carry her weight.
Now from boney sockets
she stares out on this
cruel luxuriance.

HEAT

by Gilberto Gonzalez y Contreras
(El Salvador) [1904–   ]

TRANSLATED FROM THE SPANISH
BY DUDLEY FITTS

Tropical mid-day. Indolence.
The reddish nudity
of the plowed field
begs the coconut-tree
to wave its palmy fan.

The creaking wood
mimics the cicada.
Silence walks on tiptoe
through the house.
And the water in the ditch takes the pulse
of the languid heat.

OMEN
by Birago Diop (Africa) [1906–   ]

A naked sun—a yellow sun
A sun all naked at early dawn
Pours waves of gold over the bank
Of the river of yellow.

A naked sun—a white sun
A sun all naked and white
Pours waves of silver
Over the river of white.

A naked sun—a red sun
A sun all naked and red
Pours waves of red blood
Over the river of red.

DATES

from The Thousand and One Nights

[*Thirteenth century* A.D.]

TRANSLATED FROM THE ARABIAN
BY POWYS MATHERS

We grow to the sound of the wind
Playing his flutes in our hair,

Palm tree daughters,
Brown flesh Bedouin,
Fed with light
By our gold father;

We are loved of the free-tented,
The sons of space, the hall-forgetters,
The wide-handed, the bright-sworded
Masters of horses.

Who has rested in the shade of our palms
Shall hear us murmur ever above his sleep.

GRAPES

by Alexander Pushkin [1799–1837]

TRANSLATED FROM THE RUSSIAN
BY BABETTE DEUTSCH AND AVRAHM YARMOLINSKY

I shall not miss the roses, fading
When springtime's hurrying days are done;
I love the grapes whose clusters ripen
Upon the hillsides in the sun—
The glory of my fertile valley,
They hang, each lustrous as a pearl,
Gold autumn's joy, oblong, transparent,
Like the slim fingers of a girl.

IT RAINED IN THE NIGHT

by Jorge Carrera Andrade (Ecuador) [1903–   ]

TRANSLATED FROM THE SPANISH
BY MUNA LEE DE MUÑOZ MARÍN

It rained in the night—
there are pears on the ground.
Prostrate as abbesses
the cabbages lie round.

From the bird at the window
there's all this to be heard.
Out here in the country
Our newspaper's the bird.

Goodbye to worries!
Let's leave the lazy bed.
Rain has washed life as clean
as a cabbage-head.

AFTER RAIN
by Tu Fu [A.D. 712–770]

TRANSLATED FROM THE CHINESE BY CHI HWANG CHU
AND EDNA WORTHLEY UNDERWOOD

In the autumn sky the clouds are thinned.
From the west comes the wild, ten-thousand-*li* wind.
But the dawn was beautiful to see!

The long rain has not yet damaged the grain,
The Green-Willow Road seems to bend, to strain.
The mountain berries are small and red.

On the city tower the trumpets blare
And a wild goose shoots to blue deeps of air.

IN THE HILLS
by Wang Wei [A.D. 699–759]

TRANSLATED FROM THE CHINESE
BY ROBERT PAYNE

White pebbles jut from the river-stream,
Stray leaves red in the cold autumn:
No rain is falling on the mountain path,
But my clothes are damp in the fine green air.

SIGNS OF WINTER

by John Clare [1793–1864]

The cat runs races with her tail. The dog
Leaps o'er the orchard hedge and gnarls the grass.
The swine run round and grunt and play with straw,
Snatching out hasty mouthfuls from the stack.
Sudden upon the elm-tree tops the crow
Unceremonious visit pays and croaks,
Then swoops away. From mossy barn the owl
Bobs hasty out—wheels round and, scared as soon,
As hastily retires. The ducks grow wild
And from the muddy pond fly up and wheel
A circle round the village and soon, tired,
Plunge in the pond again. The maids in haste
Snatch from the orchard hedge the mizzled clothes
And laughing hurry in to keep them dry.

EXEUNT

by Richard Wilbur [1921–   ]

Piecemeal the summer dies;
At the field's edge a daisy lives alone;
A last shawl of burning lies
On a gray field-stone.

All cries are thin and terse;
The field has droned the summer's final mass;
A cricket like a dwindled hearse
Crawls from the dry grass.

SOMETHING TOLD
THE WILD GEESE
by Rachel Field [1894–1942]

Something told the wild geese
   It was time to go.
Though the fields lay golden
   Something whispered, "Snow."
Leaves were green and stirring,
   Berries, luster-glossed,
But beneath warm feathers
   Something cautioned, "Frost."
All the sagging orchards
   Steamed with amber spice,
But each wild breast stiffened
   At remembered ice.
Something told the wild geese
   It was time to fly—
Summer sun was on their wings,
   Winter in their cry.

NOVEMBER NIGHT
by Adelaide Crapsey [1878–1914]

Listen . . .
With faint dry sound,
Like steps of passing ghosts,
The leaves, frost-crisp'd, break from the trees
And fall.

WINTER MORNING

by Winifred Welles [1893–1939]

How brave, how faithful, and how frightening
To wake and find myself on earth alone,
The only mutable, dark, homely thing
Not turned to jewelry, metal, or white stone.
Sole of all rigid sleepers I am chosen
To tread my dazzled house, and to be shown
At window after window how far-frozen
The white fields gleam, how trees to glass are blown.
Oh, strangely strong I am to keep on moving
And looking at such landscapes bright in death,
To bear such solitude alive and loving,
Such stillness learn, yet never catch my breath,
Nor clasp my hands, nor feel my wide eyes smart—
This world itself will break before my heart.

BLUE WINTER

by Robert Francis [1901–   ]

Winter uses all the blues there are.
One shade of blue for water, one for ice,
Another blue for shadows over snow.
The clear or cloudy sky uses blue twice—
Both different blues. And hills row after row
Are colored blue according to how far.
You know the bluejay's double-blue device
Shows best when there are no green leaves to show.
And Sirius is a winterbluegreen star.

SHOPPING FOR MEAT
IN WINTER

by Oscar Williams [1900–1966]

What lewd, naked and revolting shape is this?
A frozen oxtail in the butcher's shop
Long and lifeless upon the huge block of wood
On which the ogre's axe begins *chop chop*.

The sun like incense fumes on the smoky glass,
The street frets with people, the winter wind
Throws knives, prices dangle from shoppers' mouths
While the grim vegetables, on parade, bring to mind

The great countryside bathed in golden sleep,
The trees, the bees, the soft peace everywhere—
I think of the cow's tail, how all summer long
It beat the shapes of harps into the air.

THE PINE BOUGH
by Richard Aldridge [1930–   ]

I saw a thing, and stopped to wonder—
For who had set the moment when
The pine bough should dip out from under
The white oppressor's arm of snow,
And upward fling itself, as though
Attracted to a blue May heaven?

THE MARCH PROBLEM
by George Garrett [1929–   ]

The wind became a green idea.
The crows were out of place.
That color didn't suit their taste
or advance their bleak career.

The concept started to careen.
They plead a fervent case.
The wind became a green idea.
The crows were out of place.

It was wonderful to hear
them flaunt against their fate;
two shrill ascetics, born too late,
denounced the Technicolor leer.
The wind became a green idea.

THAW
by Edward Thomas [1878–1917]

Over the land freckled with snow half-thawed
The speculating rooks at their nests cawed
And saw from elm-tops, delicate as flowers of grass,
What we below could not see, Winter pass.

POMONA
by William Morris [1834–1896]

I am the ancient Apple-Queen,
As once I was so am I now.
For evermore a hope unseen,
Betwixt the blossom and the bough.

Ah, where's the river's hidden gold?
And where the windy grave of Troy?
Yet come I as I came of old,
From out the heart of summer's joy.

THE SOWER

by R. Olivares Figueroa (Venezuela) [*1893–*   ]

TRANSLATED FROM THE SPANISH
BY DUDLEY FITTS

On a white field,
black little seeds . . .
> *Let it rain! rain.*

"Sower, what do you sow?"
How the furrow sings!
> *Let it rain! rain!*

"I sow rainbows,
dawns and trumpets!"
> *Let it rain! rain!*

A TRAPPED FLY

by Robert Herrick [*1591–1674*]

I saw a Fly within a Bead
Of Amber cleanly buried:
The urn was little, but the room
More rich than Cleopatra's Tomb.

THE FOUNTAIN
by al-Mu'tamid [1040–1095]

TRANSLATED FROM THE ARABIAN
BY DULCIE L. SMITH

The sea hath tempered it; the mighty sun
Polished the blade,
And from the limpid sheath the sword leaps forth;
Man hath not made
A better in Damascus—though for slaughter
Hath steel somewhat advantage over water.

IRON
by Bertolt Brecht [1898–1956]

TRANSLATED FROM THE GERMAN
BY MICHAEL HAMBURGER

In a dream last night
I saw a great gale rage.
It gripped the scaffolding
Tore down the supports
Of solid iron.
But whatever was made of wood
Bent and remained.

BITS OF GLASS

by Spencer Brown [1909–   ]

Green, brown, or gray, old bottle-shards
Are shaped by surf and scraped by sand
To soft big jewels bent or round
With bubbles delicately inblown,
Harmless to bare foot on the beach.
Lifted and held in hand like words,
They are dust-silver to the touch;
But re-immersed, their colors shine,
And a quick smash on iron or stone
Brings back the jagged scalpel's edge.

ROUNDELAY

by Isabella Gardner

A blood-red bird with one green eye
and one gilt wing is hanging high.
Slung by the neck on a Christmas tree
dangling there in the tinsel he
is not about to sing for me.

The tree it trembles, the glass gauds swing
like that bird with his one gilt wing
who bows his beak, whose one eye glows
as back and forth and round he goes
to grace notes and arpeggios.

ANECDOTE OF THE JAR

by Wallace Stevens [1879–1955]

I placed a jar in Tennessee,
And round it was, upon a hill.
It made the slovenly wilderness
Surround that hill.

The wilderness rose up to it,
And sprawled around, no longer wild.
The jar was round upon the ground
And tall and of a port in air.

It took dominion everywhere.
The jar was gray and bare.
It did not give of bird or bush,
Like nothing else in Tennessee.

ROOT CELLAR

by Theodore Roethke [1908–1963]

Nothing would sleep in that cellar, dank as a ditch,
Bulbs broke out of boxes hunting for chinks in the dark,
Shoots dangled and drooped,
Lolling obscenely from mildewed crates,
Hung down long yellow evil necks, like tropical snakes.
And what a congress of stinks!—
Roots ripe as old bait,
Pulpy stems, rank, silo-rich,
Leaf-mold, manure, lime, piled against slippery planks.
Nothing would give up life:
Even the dirt kept breathing a small breath.

VARIATION ON A SENTENCE

There are few or no bluish animals. . . .
Thoreau's Journals, Feb. 21, 1855

by Louise Bogan [1897–   ]

Of white and tawny, black as ink,
Yellow, and undefined, and pink,
And piebald, there are droves, I think.

(Buff kine in herd, gray whales in pod,
Brown woodchucks, colored like the sod,
All creatures from the hand of God.)

And many of a hellish hue;
But, for some reason hard to view,
Earth's bluish animals are few.

FLYING CROOKED

by Robert Graves [1895–   ]

The butterfly, a cabbage-white
(His honest idiocy of flight)
Will never now, it is too late,
Master the art of flying straight,
Yet has—who knows so well as I?—
A just sense of how not to fly:
He lurches here and there by guess
And God and hope and hopelessness.
Even the aerobatic swift
Has not his flying-crooked gift.

44

MOTH
by Kenneth Slade Alling [1887–1966]

The saffron moth
The antlered thing,
With pale gold fur
And patterned wing,
In silence sings the song
It is not given bird to sing.

THE HERON
by Theodore Roethke [1908–1963]

The heron stands in water where the swamp
Has deepened to the blackness of a pool,
Or balances with one leg on a hump
Of marsh grass heaped above a musk-rat hole.

He walks the shallow with an antic grace.
The great feet break the ridges of the sand,
The long eye notes the minnow's hiding place.
His beak is quicker than a human hand.

He jerks a frog across his bony lip,
Then points his heavy bill above the wood.
The wide wings flap but once to lift him up.
A single ripple starts from where he stood.

PIED BEAUTY

by Gerard Manley Hopkins [1844–1889]

Glory be to God for dappled things—
    For skies of couple-color as a brindled cow;
        For rose-moles all in stipple upon trout that swim;
Fresh-firecoal chestnut-falls; finches' wings;
    Landscape plotted and pieced—fold, fallow, and plough;
        And all trades, their gear and tackle and trim.
All things counter, original, spare, strange;
    Whatever is fickle, freckled (who knows how?)
        With swift, slow; sweet, sour; adazzle, dim;
He fathers-forth whose beauty is past change:
                Praise him.

THE TORTOISE IN ETERNITY
by Elinor Wylie [1885–1928]

Within my house of patterned horn
I sleep in such a bed
As men may keep before they're born
And after they are dead.

Sticks and stones may break their bones,
And words may make them bleed;
There is not one of them who owns
An armour to his need.

Tougher than hide or lozenged bark,
Snow-storm and thunder proof,
And quick with sun, and thick with dark,
Is this my darling roof.

Men's troubled dreams of death and birth
Pulse mother-o'-pearl to black;
I bear the rainbow bubble Earth
Square on my scornful back.

DESIGN
by Robert Frost [1874–1963]

I found a dimpled spider, fat and white,
On a white heal-all, holding up a moth
Like a white piece of rigid satin cloth—
Assorted characters of death and blight
Mixed ready to begin the morning right,
Like the ingredients of a witches' broth—
A snow-drop spider, a flower like a froth,
And dead wings carried like a paper kite.

What had that flower to do with being white,
The wayside blue and innocent heal-all?
What brought the kindred spider to that height,
Then steered the white moth thither in the night?
What but design of darkness to appall?—
If design govern in a thing so small.

CAPE ANN
by T. S. Eliot [1888–1965]

O quick quick quick quick hear the song-sparrow,
Swamp-sparrow, fox-sparrow, vesper-sparrow
At dawn and dusk. Follow the dance
Of the goldfinch at noon. Leave to chance
The Blackburnian warbler, the shy one. Hail
With shrill whistle the note of the quail, the bob-white
Dodging by bay-bush. Follow the feet
Of the walker, the water-thrush. Follow the flight
Of the dancing arrow, the purple martin. Greet
In silence the bullbat. All are delectable. Sweet sweet
   sweet
But resign this land at the end, resign it
To its true owner, the tough one, the sea-gull.
The palaver is finished.

THE HARBOR

by Carl Sandburg [1878–1967]

Passing through huddled and ugly walls,
By doorways when women haggard
Looked from their hunger-deep eyes,
Haunted with shadows of hunger-hands,
Out from the huddled and ugly walls,
I came sudden, at the city's edge,
On a blue burst of lake—
Long lake waves breaking under the sun
On a spray-flung curve of shore;
And a fluttering storm of gulls,
Masses of great gray wings
And flying white bellies
Veering and wheeling free in the open.

A TALISMAN

by Marianne Moore [1887–   ]

Under a splintered mast.
Torn from the ship and cast
  Near her hull,

A stumbling shepherd found,
Embedded in the ground,
  A seagull

Of lapis lazuli,
A scarab of the sea
  With wings spread—

Curling its coral feet,
Parting its beak to greet
  Men long dead.

THE DISMANTLED SHIP
by Walt Whitman [1819–1892]

In some unused lagoon, some nameless bay,
On sluggish, lonesome waters, anchor'd near the shore,
An old, dismasted, gray and batter'd ship, disabled, done,
After free voyages to all the seas of earth, haul'd up
      at last and hawser'd tight,
Lies rusting, mouldering.

FLOWERS BY THE SEA
by *William Carlos Williams* [1883–1963]

When over the flowery, sharp pasture's
edge, unseen, the salt ocean

lifts its form—chickory and daisies
tied, released, seem hardly flowers alone

but color and the movement—or the shape
perhaps—of restlessness, whereas

the sea is circled and sways
peacefully upon its plantlike stem

THE FREEDOM OF THE MOON
by Robert Frost [1874–1963]

I've tried the new moon tilted in the air
Above a hazy tree-and-farmhouse cluster
As you might try a jewel in your hair.
I've tried it fine with little breadth of luster,
Alone, or in one ornament combining
With one first-water star almost as shining.

I put it shining anywhere I please.
By walking slowly on some evening later,
I've pulled it from a crate of crooked trees
And brought it over glossy water, greater,
And dropped it in, and seen the image wallow,
The color run, all sorts of wonder follow.

WHEN I HEARD THE
LEARN'D ASTRONOMER
by Walt Whitman [1819–1892]

When I heard the learn'd astronomer,
When the proofs, the figures, were ranged in
    columns before me,
When I was shown the charts and diagrams, to add,
    divide, and measure them,
When I sitting heard the astronomer where he
    lectured with much applause in the lecture-room,
How soon unaccountable I became tired and sick,
Till rising and gliding out I wander'd off by myself,
In the mystical moist night-air, and from time to time,
Look'd up in perfect silence at the stars.

EL HOMBRE
by William Carlos Williams [1883–1963]

It's a strange courage
you give me ancient star:

Shine alone in the sunrise
toward which you lend no part!

EUCLID

by Vachel Lindsay [1879–1931]

Old Euclid drew a circle
On a sand-beach long ago.
He bounded and enclosed it
With angles thus and so.
His set of solemn graybeards
Nodded and argued much
Of arc and of circumference,
Diameter and such.
A silent child stood by them
From morning until noon
Because they drew such charming
Round pictures of the moon.

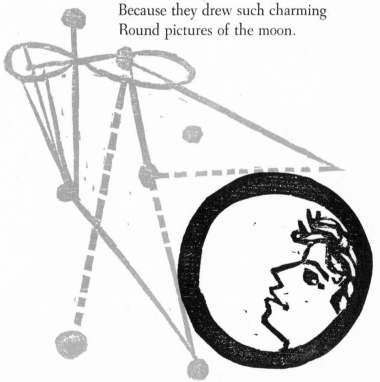

INCIDENT

by Countee Cullen [1903–1946]

Once riding in old Baltimore
    Heart-filled, head-filled with glee,
I saw a Baltimorean
    Keep looking straight at me.

Now I was eight and very small,
    And he was no whit bigger,
And so I smiled, but he poked out
    His tongue, and called me, "Nigger."

I saw the whole of Baltimore
    From May until December;
Of all the things that happened there
    That's all that I remember.

ROUGH

by Stephen Spender [1909–   ]

My parents kept me from children who were rough
Who threw words like stones and who wore torn clothes.
Their thighs showed through rags. They ran in the street
And climbed cliffs and stripped by the country streams.

I feared more than tigers their muscles like iron
Their jerking hands and their knees tight on my arms.
I feared the salt coarse pointing of those boys
Who copied my lisp behind me on the road.

They were lithe, they sprang out behind hedges
Like dogs to bark at my world. They threw mud
While I looked the other way, pretending to smile.
I longed to forgive them, but they never smiled.

BALLET SCHOOL
by Babette Deutsch [1895–   ]

Fawns in the winter wood
Who feel their horns, and leap,
Swans whom the bleakening mood
Of evening stirs from sleep,
Tall flowers that unfurl
As a moth, driven, flies,
Flowers with the breast of a girl
And sea-cold eyes.
The bare bright mirrors glow
For their enchanted shapes.
Each is a flame, and so,
Like flame, escapes.

SKIER

by Robert Francis [1901–   ]

He swings down like the flourish of a pen
Signing a signature in white on white.

The silence of his skis reciprocates
The silence of the world around him.

Wind is his one competitor
In the cool winding and unwinding down.

On incandescent feet he falls
Unfalling, trailing white foam, white fire.

THE WOMEN OF YUEH

by Li Po [A.D. 701–762]

TRANSLATED FROM THE CHINESE
BY ROBERT PAYNE

The jade faces of the girls on Yueh Stream,
Their dusky brows, their red skirts,
Each wearing a pair of golden spiked sandals—
O, their feet are white like frost.

UPON JULIA'S CLOTHES
by Robert Herrick [1591–1674]

Whenas in silks my Julia goes,
Then, then methinks, how sweetly flows
The liquefaction of her clothes!

Next, when I cast mine eyes and see
That brave vibration each way free,
—O how that glittering taketh me!

IN LESS THAN TWO
AND TWENTY YEARS

by Asclepiades of Samos [*c. 290* B.C.]

TRANSLATED FROM THE GREEK
BY WILLIAM AND MARY WALLACE

In less than two and twenty years
my cares have worn me out.
The young loves laugh to see my tears;
and if I die?—without a doubt
they'll roll, unheeding, as before,
their ivory dice upon the floor.

QUESTION IN A FIELD

by Louise Bogan [1897–   ]

Pasture, stone wall, and steeple,
What most perturbs the mind:
The heart-rending homely people,
Or the horrible beautiful kind?

TAKING LEAVE OF A FRIEND

by Rihaku [Eighth century A.D.*]*

TRANSLATED FROM THE JAPANESE
BY EZRA POUND

Blue mountains to the north of the walls,
White river winding about them;
Here we must make separation
And go out through a thousand miles of dead grass.

Mind like a floating wide cloud,
Sunset like the parting of old acquaintances
Who bow over their clasped hands at a distance.
Our horses neigh to each other as we are parting.

FIFE TUNE

(6/8) for Sixth Platoon, 308th I.T.C.

by John Manifold [1915–   ]

One morning in spring
We marched from Devizes
All shapes and all sizes
Like beads on a string,
But yet with a swing
We trod the bluemetal
And full of high fettle
We started to sing.

She ran down the stair
A twelve-year-old darling
And laughing and calling
She tossed her bright hair;
Then silent to stare
At the men flowing past her—
There were all she could master
Adoring her there.

It's seldom I'll see
A sweeter or prettier;
I doubt we'll forget her
In two years or three.
And lucky he'll be
She takes for a lover
While we are far over
The treacherous sea.

CHANGING THE WHEEL
by Bertolt Brecht [1898–1956]

TRANSLATED FROM THE GERMAN
BY MICHAEL HAMBURGER

I sit on the roadside bank.
The driver changes a wheel.
I do not like the place I have come from.
I do not like the place I am going to.
Why do I watch him changing the wheel
With impatience?

TRAVELLER'S CURSE
AFTER MISDIRECTION

(FROM THE WELSH)

by Robert Graves [1895–   ]

May they stumble, stage by stage
On an endless pilgrimage,
Dawn and dusk, mile after mile,
At each and every step, a stile;
At each and every step withal
May they catch their feet and fall;
At each and every fall they take
May a bone within them break;
And may the bone that breaks within
Not be, for variation's sake,
Now rib, now thigh, now arm, now shin,
But always, without fail, THE NECK.

SILENCE

by Marianne Moore [1887–   ]

My father used to say,
'Superior people never make long visits,
have to be shown Longfellow's grave
or the glass flowers at Harvard.
Self-reliant like the cat—
that takes its prey to privacy,
the mouse's limp tail hanging like a shoelace from its
    mouth—
they sometimes enjoy solitude,
and can be robbed of speech
by speech which has delighted them.
The deepest feeling always shows itself in silence;
not in silence, but restraint.'
Nor was he insincere in saying, 'Make my house your
    inn.'
Inns are not residences.

MORNING AT THE WINDOW
by T. S. Eliot [1888–1965]

They are rattling breakfast plates in basement kitchens,
And along the trampled edges of the street
I am aware of the damp souls of housemaids
Sprouting despondently at area gates.

The brown waves of fog toss up to me
Twisted faces from the bottom of the street,
And tear from a passer-by with muddy skirts
An aimless smile that hovers in the air
And vanishes along the level of the roofs.

CLOSING OF THE RODEO
by William Jay Smith [1918–   ]

The lariat snaps; the cowboy rolls
   His pack, and mounts and rides away.
Back to the land the cowboy goes.

Plumes of smoke from the factory sway
   In the setting sun. The curtain falls,
A train in the darkness pulls away.

Goodbye, says the rain on the iron roofs.
   Goodbye, say the barber poles.
Dark drum the vanishing horses' hooves.

73

TO A POOR OLD WOMAN
by William Carlos Williams [1883–1963]

munching a plum on
the street a paper bag
of them in her hand

They taste good to her
They taste good
to her. They taste
good to her

You can see it by
the way she gives herself
to the one half
sucked out in her hand

Comforted
a solace of ripe plums
seeming to fill the air
They taste good to her

DIVINEST SENSE

by Emily Dickinson [1830–1886]

Much madness is divinest sense
To a discerning eye;
Much sense the starkest madness.
'Tis the majority
In this, as all, prevails.
Assent, and you are sane;
Demur,—you're straightway dangerous,
And handled with a chain.

NO PASSENGER WAS KNOWN TO FLEE

by Emily Dickinson [1830–1886]

No passenger was known to flee
That lodged a night in memory—
That wily subterranean Inn
Contrives that none go out again.

PRESENTIMENT
by Emily Dickinson [1830–1886]

Presentiment is that long shadow on the lawn
Indicative that suns go down;
The notice to the startled grass
That darkness is about to pass.

NIGHT CROW
by Theodore Roethke [1908–1963]

When I saw that clumsy crow
Flap from a wasted tree,
A shape in the mind rose up:
Over the gulfs of dream
Flew a tremendous bird
Further and further away
Into a moonless black,
Deep in the brain, far back.

THE NIGHT IS DARKENING ROUND ME

by Emily Brontë [1818–1848]

The night is darkening round me,
The wild winds coldly blow;
But a tyrant spell has bound me
And I cannot, cannot go.

The giant trees are bending
Their bare boughs weighed with snow,
And the storm is fast descending
And yet I cannot go.

Clouds beyond clouds above me,
Wastes beyond wastes below;
But nothing drear can move me;
I will not, cannot go.

ALL DAY I HEAR

by James Joyce [1882–1941]

All day I hear the noise of waters
    Making moan,
Sad as the sea-bird is, when going
    Forth alone,
He hears the winds cry to the waters'
    Monotone.

The grey winds, the cold winds are blowing
    Where I go.
I hear the noise of many waters
    Far below.
All day, all night, I hear them flowing
    To and fro.

THE LOST TRIBE
by Ruth Pitter [1897–   ]

How long, how long must I regret?
I never found my people yet;
I go about, but cannot find
The blood-relations of the mind.

Through my little sphere I range,
And though I wither do not change;
Must not change a jot, lest they
Should not know me on my way.

Sometimes I think when I am dead
They will come about my bed,
For my people well do know
When to come and when to go.

I know not why I am alone,
Nor where my wandering tribe is gone,
But be they few, or be they far,
Would I were where my people are!

SPACE

by William Burford [1927–   ]

In the air, instruments circle,
   Ours, theirs,
Recording, signaling the world.
But at heart we do not care.
These wonders turn ordinary.

But it is in our hearts
That we are lost or spared,
For a minute searching
Each other's faces,
The instruments traveling there;

Appearing and fading,
As this were space,
Were night and pale day.

FIRE AND ICE
by Robert Frost [1874–1963]

Some say the world will end in fire,
Some say in ice.
From what I've tasted of desire,
I hold with those who favor fire.
But if it had to perish twice,
I think I know enough of hate
To say that for destruction ice
Is also great
And would suffice.

PITY THIS BUSY MONSTER, MANUNKIND

by E. E. Cummings [1894–1962]

Pity this busy monster, manunkind,

not.   Progress is a comfortable disease:
your victim (death and life safely beyond)

plays with the bigness of his littleness
—electrons deify one razorblade
into a mountainrange; lenses extend

unwish through curving wherewhen till unwish
returns on its unself.
                        A world of made
is not a world of born—pity poor flesh

and trees, poor stars and stones, but never this
fine specimen of hypermagical

ultraomnipotence. We doctors know

a hopeless case if— listen: there's a hell
of a good universe next door; let's go

SONG OF A WOMAN ABANDONED BY THE TRIBE BECAUSE SHE IS TOO OLD TO KEEP UP WITH THEIR MIGRATION

TRANSLATED FROM SOUTHERN SHOSHONE
AMERICAN INDIAN BY MARY AUSTIN

Alas, that I should die,
That I should die now,
I who know so much!

It will miss me,
The twirling fire stick;
The fire coal between the hearth stones,
It will miss me.

The medicine songs,
The songs of magic healing;
The medicine herbs by the water borders,
They will miss me;
The basket willow,
It will miss me;
All the wisdom of women,
It will miss me.

Alas, that I should die,
Who know so much.

NAHUATL POEM

TRANSLATED FROM NAHUATL (MEXICAN INDIAN)
BY WILLIAM CARLOS WILLIAMS

Will he return will Prince Cuatli ever return?
Will Ayocuan, the one who drove an arrow into the sky?
Shall these two yet gladden you?
     Events don't recur: we vanish once only.
Hence the cause of my weeping:
Prince Ayocuan, warrior chief
governed us harshly.
His pride waxed more, he grew haughty
here among men.
     But his time is finished . . .
he can no longer come to bow down before Father and
   Mother . . .
This is the reason for my weeping:
He has fled to the place where all lack a body!

THE OLD FORT OF RATHANGAN

TRANSLATED FROM OLD IRISH
BY KUNO MEYER

The fort over against the oak-wood,
Once it was Bruidge's, it was Cathal's,
It was Aed's, it was Ailill's,
It was Conaing's, it was Ciuline's,
And it was Maelduin's;
The fort remains after each in his turn—
And the kings asleep in the ground.

EPITAPH ON ELIZABETH, L.H.
by Ben Jonson [1573?–1637]

Would'st thou hear what man can say
  In a little? Reader, stay.
Underneath this stone doth lie
  As much beauty as could die;
Which in life did harbour give
  To more virtue than doth live.
If at all she had a fault,
  Leave it buried in this vault.
One name was *Elizabeth,*
  Th' other let it sleep with death;
Fitter, where it died, to tell,
  Than that it lived at all. Farewell.

AN IRISH AIRMAN
FORESEES HIS DEATH

by William Butler Yeats [1865–1939]

I know that I shall meet my fate
Somewhere among the clouds above;
Those that I fight I do not hate,
Those that I guard I do not love;
My country is Kiltartan Cross,
My countrymen Kiltartan's poor,
No likely end could bring them loss
Or leave them happier than before.
Nor law, nor duty bade me fight,
Nor public men, nor cheering crowds,
A lonely impulse of delight
Drove to this tumult in the clouds;
I balanced all, brought all to mind,
The years to come seemed waste of breath,
A waste of breath the years behind
In balance with this life, this death.

HAZARDOUS OCCUPATIONS

by Carl Sandburg [1878–1967]

Jugglers keep six bottles in the air.
Club swingers toss up six and eight.
The knife throwers miss each other's
    ears by a hair and the steel quivers
    in the target wood.
The trapeze battlers do a back-and-forth
    high in the air with a girl's feet
    and ankles upside down.
So they earn a living—till they miss
    once, twice, even three times.
So they live on hate and love as gypsies
    live in satin skin and shiny eyes.
In their graves do the elbows jostle once
    in a blue moon—and wriggle to throw
    a kiss answering a dreamed-of applause?
Do the bones repeat: It's a *good* act—
    we got a *good* hand . . . ?

DANIEL BOONE
1735–1820

by Stephen Vincent Benet [1898–1943]

When Daniel Boone goes by, at night,
The phantom deer arise
And all lost, wild America
Is burning in their eyes.

KNOWLT HOHEIMER

by Edgar Lee Masters [1869–1950]

I was the first fruits of the battle of Missionary Ridge.
When I felt the bullet enter my heart
I wished I had staid at home and gone to jail
For stealing the hogs of Curl Trenary,
Instead of running away and joining the army.
Rather a thousand times the county jail
Than to lie under this marble figure with wings,
And this granite pedestal
Bearing the words, *"Pro Patria."*
What do they mean, anyway?

EPITAPH ON A TYRANT
by W. H. Auden [1907–   ]

Perfection, of a kind, was what he was after,
And the poetry he invented was easy to understand;
He knew human folly like the back of his hand,
And was greatly interested in armies and fleets;
When he laughed, respectable senators burst with
   laughter,
And when he cried the little children died in the streets.

90

PORTRAIT
by E. E. Cummings [1894–1962]

Buffalo Bill's
defunct
            who used to
            ride a watersmooth-silver
                                    stallion
and break onetwothreefourfive pigeonsjustlikethat
                                                Jesus

he was a handsome man
                    and what i want to know is
how do you like your blueeyed boy
Mister Death

CRUCIFORM
by Winifred Welles [1893–1939]

Here in the sand, where someone laid him down,
The one known human signature is clear.
Whether woman or man, white-skinned or brown,
Whether the outflung arms were so for fear,
Or agony, or weariness, or shame,
Here, in one line athwart another line,
Is briefly written the one mutual name,
A savior's, or a thief's, or yours, or mine.
Dunes sifted undersea long since have borne
This selfsame cross, small and anonymous.
Tan deserts that the wind has not yet worn
Will print this symbol, and not one of us
But then, or some day, could lie down and fit
Our desolate arms and bodies into it.

FUTILITY
by Wilfred Owen [1893–1918]

Move him in the sun—
Gently its touch awoke him once,
At home, whispering of fields unsown.
Always it woke him, even in France,
Until this morning and this snow.
If anything might rouse him now
The kind old sun will know.

Think how it wakes the seeds, —
Woke, once, the clays of a cold star.
Are limbs, so dear-achieved, are sides,
Full-nerved—still warm—too hard to stir?
Was it for this the clay grew tall?
—O what made fatuous sunbeams toil
To break earth's sleep at all?

TO DAFFODILS
by Robert Herrick [1591–1674]

Fair daffodils, we weep to see
   You haste away so soon;
As yet the early-rising sun
   Has not attained his noon.
     Stay, stay,
   Until the hasting day
     Has run
   But to the evensong;
And having prayed together, we
   Will go with you along.

We have short time to stay as you;
   We have as short a spring;
As quick a growth to meet decay
   As you, or anything.
     We die
   As your hours do, and dry
     Away
   Like to the summer's rain;
Or as the pearls of morning's dew
   Ne'er to be found again.

SONNET

by John Donne [1573–1631]

Death be not proud, though some have calléd thee
Mighty and dreadful, for thou art not so,
For those, whom thou think'st thou dost overthrow,
Die not, poor Death, nor yet canst thou kill me.
From rest and sleep, which but thy pictures be,
Much pleasure, then from thee much more must flow,
And soonest our best men with thee do go,
Rest of their bones, and souls' delivery.
Thou art slave to fate, chance, kings, and desperate men,
And dost with poison, war, and sickness dwell,
And poppy or charms can make us sleep as well,
And better than thy stroke; why swell'st thou then?
One short sleep past, we wake eternally,
And Death shall be no more; Death, thou shalt die.

RUMINATION

by Richard Eberhart [1904–   ]

When I can hold a stone within my hand
And feel time make it sand and soil, and see
The roots of living things grow in this land,
Pushing between my fingers flower and tree,
Then I shall be as wise as death,
For death has done this and he will
Do this to me, and blow his breath
To fire my clay, when I am still.

GO TO THE SHINE
THAT'S ON A TREE

by Richard Eberhart [1904–   ]

Go to the shine that's on a tree
When dawn has laved with liquid light
With luminous light the lighted tree
And take that glory without fright.

Go to the song that's in a bird
When he has seen the glistening tree,
That glorious tree the bird has heard
Give praise for its felicity.

Then go to the earth and touch it keen
Be tree and bird, be wide aware
Be wild aware of light unseen,
And unheard song along the air.

THE SHAPE CALLED STAR

by Louise Townsend Nicholl

A rugged star, a wreath of root
Circles the tree trunk at its foot.
Always the jaggéd shape called star,
Splintered by impact of surprise,
Marks where a miracle shall rise.
Where ground meets tree, where eye meets light,
Where any thing which comes from far
Through earth or ether makes its way
And, using root or using ray,
Startles the sphere of mortal sight,
There does the prongéd figure stretch
To keep the stranger within reach.

LEAF AND SUN

by Norma Farber

Let us who live in leafy cage
and see the flare of noon impurely
and feel the fire through foliage
let us not leave the light entirely.

Let us like watchers in a shelter
from lurking shadows look at shine,
and learn how leaf or two can alter
the large intention of the sun.

99

THE HATCH

by Norma Farber

I found myself one day
cracking the shell of sky,
peering into a place
beyond mere universe.

I broke from egg of here
into anotherwhere
wider than worldly home
I was emerging from.

I breathed, I took a step,
I looked around, and up,
and saw another lining
inside a further sky.

WATCH LONG ENOUGH, AND YOU WILL SEE THE LEAF

by Conrad Aiken [1889–   ]

Watch long enough, and you will see the leaf
Fall from the bough. Without a sound it falls:
And soundless meets the grass. . . . And so you have
A bare bough, and a dead leaf in dead grass.
Something has come and gone. And that is all.

But what were all the tumults in this action?
What wars of atoms in the twig, what ruins,
Fiery and disastrous, in the leaf?
Timeless the tumult was, but gave no sign.
Only, the leaf fell, and the bough is bare.

This is the world: there is no more than this.
The unseen and disastrous prelude, shaking
The trivial act from the terrific action.
Speak: and the ghosts of change, past and to come,
Throng the brief word. The maelstrom has us all.

A VISION
by Henry Vaughan [1622–1695]

I saw Eternity the other night,
Like a great ring of pure and endless light,
    All calm, as it was bright:—
And round beneath it, Time, in hours, days, years,
    Driven by the spheres,
Like a vast shadow moved; in which the World
    And all her train were hurl'd.

FROM FAR, FROM EVE
AND MORNING

by A. E. Housman [1859–1936]

From far, from eve and morning
   And yon twelve-winded sky,
The stuff of life to knit me
   Blew hither: here am I.

Now—for a breath I tarry
   Nor yet disperse apart—
Take my hand quick and tell me,
   What have you in your heart.

Speak now, and I will answer;
   How shall I help you, say;
Ere to the wind's twelve quarters
   I take my endless way.

INDEX OF AUTHORS

INDEX OF TITLES

INDEX OF FIRST LINES

110

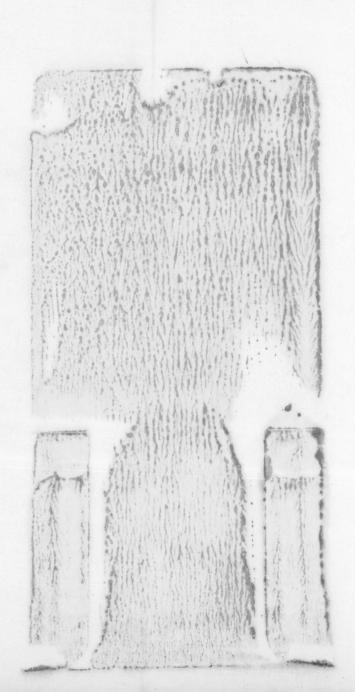